Nuffield Primary Science
SCIENCE PROCESSES AND CONCEPT EXPLORATION

Ages
5-7

The Earth in Space

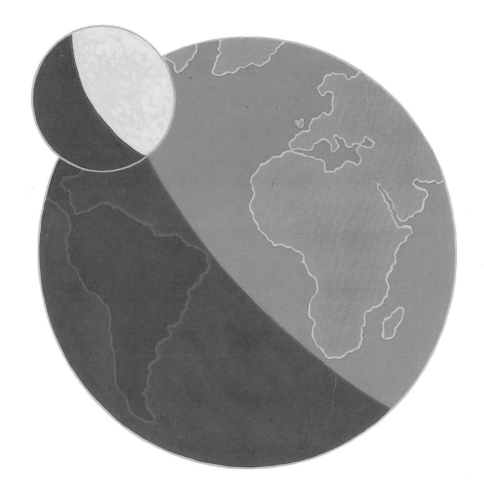

TEACHERS' GUIDE

PUBLISHED FOR THE NUFFIELD–CHELSEA CURRICULUM TRUST BY COLLINS EDUCATIONAL

Trial schools

The SPACE Project and the Trust are grateful to the governors, staff, and pupils of all the trial schools. It will be obvious to readers of these publications how much we are indebted to them for their help, and especially for the children's drawn and written records of their hard work and their growing understanding of science.

All Saints Primary School, Barnet, Hertfordshire
Arnot County Primary Infant School, Arnot Street, Walton, Liverpool
Balladen Primary School, Rawtenstall, Rossendale
Blacko County Primary School, Blacko, Lancashire
Chalgrove JMI School, Finchley, London N3
Fairway JMI School, Mill Hill, London NW7
Fazakerley Junior School, Formosa Drive, Liverpool
Foulds Primary School, Barnet, Hertfordshire
Frenchwood County Primary School, Preston, Lancashire
Hillbrook Primary School, Tooting, London SW17
Mawdesley Church of England Primary School, Lancashire
Padiham Green Church of England Primary School, Padiham, Lancashire
Roe Lee County Primary School, Blackburn, Lancashire
St Aloysius Roman Catholic Infants School, Knowsley
St Ambrose Junior School, Alderfield Drive, Speke, Liverpool
St Hughes RC JMI School, Earle Road, Liverpool
St Michael in the Hamlet Infant School, Neilson Road, Liverpool
St Stephen's Church of England School, Burnley
St Theresa's Roman Catholic Primary School, Finchley, London N3
Salterforth Primary School, Salterforth, Lancashire
Snaresbrook Primary School, Wanstead, London E18
Stubbins Primary School, Ramsbottom, Lancashire
Thorn County Primary School, Cowtoot Lane, Bacup, Lancashire
Trawden County Primary School, Dean Street, Trawden, Lancashire
Walton-le-Dale County Primary School, Preston
Water County Primary School, Burnley Road East, Water, Rossendale
Waterfoot County Primary School, Thornfield Avenue, Waterfoot, Rossendale
Whittlefield Infant School, Tabor Street, Burnley, Lancashire
Woodridge Primary School, North Finchley, London N12

Contents

Explanation of symbols in the margins

 Warning

 Good opportunities to develop and assess work related to Experimental and Investigative Science.

 Notes which may be useful to the teacher

 Vocabulary work

 Opportunities for children to use information technology

 Equipment needed

 Reference to the pupils' books

Planning

1.1 The SPACE approach to teaching and learning science

A primary class where the SPACE approach to science is being used may not at first seem different from any other class engaged in science activities; in either, children will be mentally and physically involved in exploring objects and events in the world around them. However, a closer look will reveal that both the children's activities and the teacher's role differ from those found in other approaches. The children are not following instructions given by others; they are not solving a problem set them by someone else. They are deeply involved in work which is based on their own ideas, and they have taken part in deciding how to do it.

The teacher has, of course, prepared carefully to reach the point where children try out their ideas. She or he will have started on the topic by giving children opportunities to explore from their own experience situations which embody important scientific ideas. The teacher will have ensured that the children have expressed their ideas about what they are exploring, using one or more of a range of approaches – from whole class discussion to talking with individual children, or asking children to write or draw – and will have explored the children's reasons for having those ideas.

With this information the teacher will have decided how to help the children to develop or revise their ideas. That may involve getting the children to use the ideas to make a prediction, then testing it by seeing if it works in practice; or the children may gather further evidence to discuss and think about. In particular, the teacher will note how 'scientific' children have been in their gathering and use of evidence; and should, by careful questioning, encourage greater rigour in the use of scientific process skills.

It is essential that it is the children who change their ideas as a result of what they find themselves, and that they are not merely accepting ideas which they are told are better.

By carefully exploring children's ideas, taking them seriously and choosing appropriate ways of helping the children to test them, the teacher can move children towards ideas which apply more widely and fit the evidence better – those which are, in short, more scientific.

You will find more information about the SPACE approach in the Nuffield Primary Science *Science Co-ordinators' handbook*.

1.2 Useful strategies

Finding out children's ideas

This guide points out many opportunities for finding out children's ideas. One way is simply by talking, but there are many others. We have found the following strategies effective. How you use them may depend on the area of science you are dealing with. In the teachers' guides you will find examples of these strategies, with suggestions as to where you might use them. More information about them is given in the *Science Co-ordinators' handbook*.

Talking and open questioning

Whole class discussions can be useful for sharing ideas, but they do not always give all children a chance to speak. It is often helpful if children are allowed to think of their own ideas first, perhaps working them out in drawings, and are then encouraged to share these with others – perhaps with just one other child, or with a larger group.

Annotated drawings

Asking children to draw their ideas can give a particularly clear insight into what they think. It also gives you a chance to discuss the children's ideas with them. Words conveying these ideas can then be added to the drawing, either by you or by the child, in the course of discussion to clarify what has been represented. Such work can be kept as a permanent record.

Sorting and classifying

This can be a useful way of helping children to clarify their ideas and to record their thinking. They could sort a collection of objects or pictures into groups.

Writing down ideas

When they have acquired some writing skill, this gives children the opportunity to express their own views. It will usually be in response to questions posed by you.

Log books and diaries

These can be used to record changes over a longer period of time. They need not necessarily be kept by individual children, but could be kept by a group or class as a whole. Children can jot down, as words or drawings, the changes they notice and something about what they think are the reasons for what they observe.

Helping children to develop their ideas

Letting children try out their own ideas

This will involve children in using some of the process skills of science: at first mainly observing, predicting, and communicating. Later, as children approach Key Stage 2, they will begin to make more use of measuring, hypothesizing, planning and carrying out fair tests, and interpreting results and findings.

As often as possible, children should see what happens when they put their ideas to test. They should be encouraged to observe and report carefully what happens and to give their ideas about why it happens.

Encouraging generalization from one context to another

In discussing a particular event, for example dissolving sugar in tea, consider whether the explanation proposed applies in another context, such as salt dissolving on a wet road. You or the children might suggest other contexts where the idea might be tried. This might be done by discussing the evidence for and against the explanation, or by gathering more evidence and testing the idea in the other context, depending on children's familiarity with the events being examined.

Discussing the words children use to describe their ideas

Children can be asked to be quite specific about the meaning of words they use, whether scientific or not. They can be prompted to think of alternative words which have almost the same meaning. They can be asked to think of examples of a word they are using, such as 'melt', so that you can decide when to introduce alternative or more precise words if necessary.

Extending the range of evidence

Some of the children's ideas may be consistent with their experience up to that time, but they could be challenged by extending the range of this experience. This applies particularly to things which are not easily observed, such as slow changes; or those which are normally hidden, such as the insides of objects. Books are useful in some cases.

Getting children to communicate their ideas

Expressing ideas in any way – through writing, drawing, modelling or, particularly, through discussion – involves thinking them through, and often rethinking and revising them. Discussion has a further advantage in that it is two-way and children can set others' ideas against their own. Just realizing that there are different ideas helps them to reconsider their own.

1.3 Charts to help children to develop their ideas

The charts on pages 18, 28 and 37 show how you can help children to develop their ideas from starting points which have given rise to different ideas.

The centre rectangles contain starter questions.
The surrounding 'thought bubbles' contain the sort of ideas expressed by children.
The further ring of rectangles contains questions posed by teachers in response to the ideas expressed by the children. These questions are meant to prompt children to think about their ideas.
The outer rounded boxes indicate ways in which the children might respond to the teacher's questions.
Some of the shapes have been left blank, as a sign that other ideas may be encountered and other ways of helping children to develop their ideas may be tried.

1.4 The Earth in Space and the curriculum

This teachers' guide is divided into themes; in each one there is a section on finding out children's ideas, examples of ideas children have, and a section on helping children to develop their ideas.

Time

This theme helps children come to a better understanding of time.

Many young children have little experience of judging and quantifying time periods. Consequently, they may have difficulty in gauging the length of a period of time in time units.

This theme includes activities which help children become more aware of the passage of time, develops their ideas about the units and measurement of time, and improves their skills in judging time periods. The activities include constructing time lines, designing timing devices, measuring time intervals and investigating how the time of day can be estimated from a sundial.

Many of the ideas developed here are fundamental to investigations in other themes.

National Curriculum Programme of Study

Time appears in the Mathematics National Curriculum at Key Stage 1 (Ma3:4a). Pupils should be taught to begin to use a wider range of standard units of time.

Environmental Studies 5-14 (Scotland): Science

Understanding Earth and Space

Earth in Space
Leading on to (Stages P4 to P6)
• the planets of the solar system;
• measuring the passage of time.

Earth, Sun and Moon

This theme helps children find out about the Earth, Sun and Moon.

Some young children are aware that the Sun appears to move in the sky and that the appearance of the Moon changes. However, many are unable to describe these changes in detail, or to relate changes to the movement of the Earth and Moon.

Children are encouraged to observe changes in the sky, and to find out how these changes can be explained. Children will think about models of the Earth, Moon and Sun to explore their ideas. They will seek explanations of their observations in a variety of secondary sources and compare their ideas with those from different cultures.

Seasonal change

Young children often explain the differences between summer and winter by simply referring to temperature changes, or to the type of clothes they wear. Others may describe changes in animal and plant life, or in human activities. Many children suggest that all plants are dead in winter, and that there is no Sun in the sky. Very few children describe changes in day length or how the altitude of the Sun varies from season to season.

This theme includes suggestions for helping children to associate each season with plant and animal life cycles, the supply of particular foods, human activities and celebrations, weather patterns and the position of the Sun in the sky.

The work in this theme helps children to become more aware of the differences between the seasons and the importance of the Sun in seasonal changes.

This theme prepares children for work in Key Stage 2 on the Earth and beyond (Sc4a).

Seasonal change now appears in the Geography National Curriculum at Key Stage 1, not science. Pupils should be taught about the effects of weather on people and their surroundings (5c).

Understanding Earth and Space

Earth in Space
Leading on to (Stages P4 to P6)
• the planets of the solar system;
• measuring the passage of time.

Understanding Earth and Space

On planet Earth
Leading on to (Stages P4 to P6)
• patterns of weather observed locally.

1.5 Experimental and Investigative Science

Two important aspects of children's learning in science are:

◆ learning how to investigate the world around them;
◆ learning to make sense of the world around them using scientific ideas.

These are reflected in the National Curriculum. 'Experimental and Investigative Science' covers the first aspect. The second aspect is covered by the rest of the Programme of Study. Although these two aspects of science learning are separated in the National Curriculum they cannot be separated in practice and it is not useful to try to do so. Through investigation children explore their ideas and/or test out the ideas which arise from discussion. As a result, ideas may be advanced, but this will depend on the children's investigation skills. Thus it is important to develop these skills in the context of activities which extend ideas. So there is no separate Nuffield Primary Science teachers' guide on scientific investigations, because opportunities to make these occur throughout all the guides and they form an essential part of the SPACE approach.

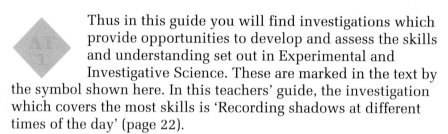 Thus in this guide you will find investigations which provide opportunities to develop and assess the skills and understanding set out in Experimental and Investigative Science. These are marked in the text by the symbol shown here. In this teachers' guide, the investigation which covers the most skills is 'Recording shadows at different times of the day' (page 22).

It is important that teachers give active guidance to pupils during investigations to help them work out how to improve the way in which they plan and carry out their investigations.

Experimental and Investigative Science is about the ways scientific evidence can be obtained, about the ways observations and measurements are made, and about the way in which the evidence is analysed. It therefore sets out three main ways in which pupils can develop their ability to do experimental and investigative science, as follows:-

1 'Planning experimental work'. Here, children should be helped to make progress from asking general and vague questions, to suggesting ideas which could be tested. Teachers' discussion with pupils should aim to help them to make predictions, using their existing understanding, on the basis of which they can decide what evidence should be collected. This should lead them to think about what apparatus and equipment they should use.

When children describe plans for their work, they should be helped to think about what features they are going to change, what effects of these changes they are going to observe or measure, and what features they must keep the same. In this way they can come to understand what is meant by 'a fair test'.

2   'Obtaining evidence'. Children should make observations in the light of their ideas about what they are looking for and why. When they describe their observations, teachers may have to help them to improve, for example by reminding them of their original aims and plan for the work. Such help should also encourage progress from qualitative comparisons and judgements to appreciating the value of making quantitative measurements (for example 'cold water' is qualitative, 'water at 12°C' is quantitative). This should lead to the development of skills with a variety of instruments and to increasing care and accuracy in measurement, involving, for example, repeating measurements to check.

3   'Considering evidence'. Here, children should first learn to record their evidence in systematic and clear ways, starting with simple drawings and then learning to use tables, bar charts and line graphs to display the patterns in numerical data. Then they should be asked to think about and discuss their results, considering what might be learnt from any trends or patterns. As ideas develop, they should be careful in checking their evidence against the original idea underlying the investigation and should become increasingly critical in discussing alternative explanations which might fit their evidence. In such discussions, they should be helped to relate their arguments to their developing scientific understanding. They should also be guided to see possibilities for conducting their investigation more carefully, or in quite different ways.

Whilst these three may seem to form a natural sequence of stages, children's work might not follow this particular sequence. For example, some might start with evidence from their observations and proceed on this basis to propose a hypothesis and a plan to test it. For others, the results of one task may be the starting point for a new inquiry involving new measurements. Useful learning about how to investigate might arise when only one or two of the above aspects of an investigation are involved, or when the teacher tells children about some aspects so that they can concentrate on others. However, there should be some occasions for all pupils when they carry out the whole process of investigation by themselves.

The assessment examples given in chapter 3 are analysed in relation to the level descriptions, which describe children's progress in relation to these three aspects: *planning experimental work*, *obtaining evidence* and *considering evidence*. Thus, these three provide a framework both for guiding children and for assessing their progress in experimental and investigative work.

1.6 Planning your science programme in school

The following pages give examples of how two schools have planned their science programme for the whole of Key Stage 1. Planning of this kind helps to provide continuity and progression in children's learning in science. The development of such whole school programmes is discussed more fully in the *Science Co-ordinators' Handbook*.

Each plan covers the requirements for the National Curriculum at Key Stage 1 and shows which themes in the Nuffield Primary Science Teachers' Guides have been used for planning the topic in detail by the classteacher.

Example 1

This primary school has recently grown from 1.5 form entry to 2 form entry and so have had to take account of varying class sizes and vertical grouping. Their programme is based on fixed year topics which provide progression through the programme of study but by using the SPACE approach staff feel they are able to cater for individual children.

Each topic is planned out, by year group, in terms of the concept to be explored and the key ideas to be focused on using the Teachers' Guides. Some topics run for one term whilst others are restricted to half a term. A minimum of five lessons are allowed for each half term. Individual teachers use the topic plan to develop their own short term planning responding to the ideas of the children in their class.

	AUTUMN TERM	SPRING TERM		SUMMER TERM	
RECEPTION	Individual variation	Sources and uses of electricity	Light and dark	Changing materials	
Nuffield Primary Science Teachers' Guide	The variety of life 2.2	Electricity and magnetism 2.1	Light 2.1, 2.2	Materials 2.2	
Programme of Study †	Sc2:4a	Sc4:1a	Sc4:3a, b	Sc3:2a, b; Sc4:2d	
YEAR 1	Pushes and pulls	Making and hearing sounds	The human body and keeping healthy	Local habitats	Plants and animal growth
Nuffield Primary Science Teachers' Guide	Forces and movement 2.1 Using energy 2.2	Sound and music 2	Living processes 2.2	Living things in their environment 2.1 Rocks, soil and weather 2.1 Earth in space 2.3	Living processes 2.3
Programme of Study †	Sc4:2a, b, c, d	Sc4:3c, d, e	Sc2:2a, b, c, d, e, f	Sc2:5a, b	Sc2:2e; 3a, b, c
YEAR 2	Properties of materials	Magnets	Electricity - simple circuits	Naming and grouping living things	
Nuffield Primary Science Teachers' Guide	Materials 2.1 Rocks, soil and weather 2.1	Electricity and magnetism 2.3	Electricity and magnetism 2.2	The variety of life 2.1	
Programme of Study †	Sc3:1a, b, c, d, e	Sc3:1b, c	Sc4:1a, b, c	Sc2:1a, b; 4b	

Example 2

Situated in a large conurbation this primary school is 2.5 form entry but the number of children entering fluctuates from year to year causing difficulties with class size. The Nursery is an integral part of the school and work is shared with the Reception classes. Therefore this pre-YR1 time is planned as a whole providing a wide range of experiences for the children so that they are 'working towards' the requirements of the programme of study.

The plan is set out by year group and the different elements of the Programme of Study, covering five topics per year with each one to be covered in approximately half a term. Each year group decides the order of their topics during the year. The provision of a 'spare' half term allows teachers some flexibility in their planning and, if they wish, to introduce other aspects of science not prescribed by the National Curriculum.

	AUTUMN TERM		SPRING TERM		SUMMER TERM	
RECEPTION	This is me	Our school	Plants and animals	Homes - using electricity	Toys	
Nuffield Primary Science Teachers' Guide	The variety of life 2.2	Living things in their environment 2.3	Living things in their environment 2.1; Living processes 2.3	Electricity and magnetism 2.1	Forces and movement 2.1	
Programme of Study (working toward) †	Sc2:2a, b, f; 4a	Sc2:1a, 3b, 5a; Sc3:2a	Sc2:1b, 3a, b, c, 4b, 5a, b	Sc4:1a, 3a, b	Sc4:2a, b, c	
YEAR 1	Ourselves	Growing things	Materials - clothes	Sounds/Night and day	Floating and sinking	
Nuffield Primary Science Teachers' Guide	Living processes 2.2; Variety of life 2.2	Living processes 2.3	Materials 2.1	Sound and music 2; The earth in space 2.1	Forces and movement 2.2	
Programme of Study †	Sc2:1b; 2a, b, e, f; 4a, b	Sc2:3a, b, c	Sc3:1a, b, c, d, e; 2a	Sc4:3c, d, e	Sc3:1a, c, e; Sc4:2a	
YEAR 2	Keeping healthy	Habitats	Materials - homes	Light and electricity	Moving things	
Nuffield Primary Science Teachers' Guide	Living processes 2.2	The variety of life 2.1; Living things in their environment 2.1; Rocks, soil and weather 2.1	Materials 2.1; 2.2	Electricity and magnetism 2.1, 2.2; Light 2.1; 2.2	Forces and movement 2.1; Using energy 2.2	
Programme of Study †	Sc2:1b; 2b, c, d	Sc2:4b; 5a, b	Sc3:1a, b, c, d, e; 2b	Sc4:1a, b, c; 3a, b	Sc4:2a, b, c, d	

† For the purposes of these charts the references to sections of the Programme of Study have been abbreviated as follows:

Sc2 = Life Processes and Living Things

Sc3 = Materials and their Properties

Sc4 = Physical Processes

1.7 Planning a topic

Here is a case study which may help you in planning a topic.

Case study: Journeys

A class of Year 2 children were considering science within the cross-curricular theme of journeys. The teacher planned that this topic would cover in particular the Earth's place in the universe as well as strands in Life and living processes. Children studied journeys into Space and journeys made by animals moving from one habitat to another. The topic was introduced by focusing firstly on the familiar journeys children made, and gradually introducing journeys to other parts of the world and journeys into Space. The home corner was turned into a space station for the duration of the topic. Some links were made with Maths, History, and Geography.

SCIENCE

Earth, Sun and Moon

◆ Children were asked to draw what they might notice if they journeyed into space in a rocket.

◆ They looked at a globe and different shapes, and talked about the shape of the Earth, Sun and Moon.

◆ They recorded the changing position of the Sun in the sky (with care!) and discussed what they had noticed. They exchanged ideas about how night occurs.

Habitats

◆ Children explored two different habitats and recorded the animals and plants living in the habitats.

◆ They discussed why the habitats were a good place for the animals to live.

◆ Pictures of animals in other habitats were collected and discussed. The reasons why animals such as birds move from one habitat to another were explored.

LINKS WITH OTHER CURRICULUM AREAS

History

◆ Children listened to fictional and factual stories of journeys.

Geography

◆ People who were currently on journeys because of war were considered as well as fairground people who were travelling locally.

◆ Children described the different journeys they made. They considered the different modes of transport used for each journey.

◆ They discussed why people make journeys, such as travelling to work, school, holidays, visiting friends.

◆ Postcards of visits children had made to other places led to comparisons between the area surrounding the school and holiday resorts.

Maths

Children were involved in handling different data.

◆ How many people travelled to school in a bus/car?

◆ Graphs were made of the ways children journeyed to school.

1.8 Pupils' books

The pupils' book accompanying this guide is called *A First look at Time and Space*. The pupils' books are intended to be used spread by spread. The spreads are not sequential, and they are covered in these notes in thematic order.

Features of the pupils' books include:
◆ Stimulus spreads, often visual, designed to raise questions, arouse curiosity, and to promote discussion.

◆ Information spreads, which give secondary source material in a clear and attractive way.

◆ Activity ideas, to form the basis of investigations to be carried out by the children.

◆ Cross-curricular spreads and stories which can act as a basis for creative writing, or spreads with a historical or creative focus.

◆ Real life examples of applications of science in the everyday world.

Telling the time pages 2–3

Purpose: To introduce the many different ways of telling the time of the day and year.
Notes: Explain the difference between analogue and digital clocks. The clock border can be used as an integral part of this spread.
Extension activities: The children could make a display of their own to show the different ways of telling the time. At the end of Key Stage 1, children will begin to learn how to tell the time.
Teachers' guide cross-references: *The Earth in Space*, pages 19-20.

Seasons pages 4–5

Purpose: A discussion spread to extend idea of seasons.
Notes: Children could say how they can tell what season it is – from the vegetation, weather, brightness of the light, clothes etc.
Extension activity: The children can use the months around the edge of the spread to match with the photographs. Clues are given on each month.
Pupils' book cross-reference: *A first look at rocks, soil and weather*, pages 22-3.
Teachers' guide cross-reference: *The Earth in Space*, pages 38-9; *Rocks, soil and weather*, page 40.

What is the time? pages 8–9

Purpose: A discussion spread to illustrate different times of day.
Note: There are no 'right' answers to the question. The position of the Sun, the length of shadows and the activity can all be used as evidence.
Extension activities: The children could think about their daily activities, and at what time of day they do them. They could make up a storyboard with their own pictures of a typical day.
Teachers' guide cross-references: *The Earth in Space*, pages 19-20.

What time of year is it? pages 10–11

Purpose: To teach children that there is a pattern to the year. Illustrate that some things happen at the same time each year.
Note: Children can apply the pictures to their own lives. For example, fireworks could be 5 November, Diwali or some other celebration.
Extension activity: Ask the children when all these events happen. There may be room for comparison if their answers differ.
Teachers' guide cross-reference: *The Earth in Space*, page 19.

Telling the time with shadows pages 12–13

Purpose: To show children that they can tell the time by their shadows.
Notes: The shadows will be shortest at midday, but longer in the morning and afternoon.
Questions for discussion: How are the shadows different in each photograph? Have you ever seen a sundial? What time does this one show? (2.30 p.m.)
Extension activities: Children could study their own shadows, perhaps drawing round them.
Pupils' book cross-reference: A first look at light, page 3.
Teachers' guide cross-reference: *The Earth in Space*, page 22.

The night-life of a town fox pages 14–15

Purpose: A story to prompt a discussion about animals that are active at night.
Question for discussion: What other animals can you think of that are active during the night? (Cats, hamsters, owls, bats etc.)
Teachers' guide cross-reference: *The Earth in Space*, page 29.

Awake at night pages 16–17

Purpose: To provide a discussion spread to follow on from the fox story and to illustrate that people are also active at night.
Questions for discussion: Can you describe the pictures? What are the people doing? Why are they so busy?
Extension activity: Ask the children if they know anyone who works during the night.
Teachers' guide cross-reference: *The Earth in Space*, page 29.

Looking at the night sky pages 6–7

Purpose: An introduction to the night sky and some common constellations.
Notes: Orion is shown because it is the most obvious winter constellation – and winter is the best time to see stars because it gets dark early.
Question for discussion: Have you ever seen any of these groups of stars?

The Moon pages 18–19

Purpose: To provide information.
Note: Explain that we know a lot about the surface of the Moon because people actually landed on it.
Question for discussion: How is the Moon different from Earth?
Teachers' guide cross-references: *The Earth in Space*, pages 10, 29-30.

A story about the moon and stars pages 20–21

Purpose: A fantasy story about the phases of the Moon.
Questions for discussion: Do you think the story is true? Why – or why not?
Extension activities: The children could listen to other traditional stories about the Moon and stars. Link this with English.
Teachers' guide cross-references: *The Earth in Space*, pages 31-2.

Times to remember pages 22–23

Purpose: Information about major festivals linked to changes in the Sun and Moon.
Extension activities: The children may be able to relate these festivals to their own experiences.
Teachers' guide cross-references: *The Earth in Space*, pages 31-2.

1.9 Resources

This is what you may need to carry out the investigations shown in this book.

Collection of 2-D and 3-D geometric shapes, including flat discs, spheres, cylinders, flat rectangles, cubes, cuboids
Bag to hold shapes
Reference books and charts which show colourful pictures of the Solar System, Earth, Sun and Moon, and which give descriptions in simple text
Globes (inflatable are particularly useful as they are fairly cheap and are large enough to be handled by a group of children)
Powerful torches
Large coloured balls

Selection of clocks, watches, calendars, diaries
Selection of materials for making simple sundials
Card tubes
Stopwatch, tocker timer, sand timer.
Selection of pictures which show seasonal scenes and activities
Story books in which there are: illustrations of the Sun, Moon and Earth; stories from different cultures about the Sun, Moon, night and day
School garden or 'wildlife' area

1.10 Warnings

Activities which need particular care are indicated by this symbol in the margin. Everything possible should be done to ensure the safety of the children during their investigations. You should consult any guidelines produced by your school or Local Education Authority and, if your school or LEA is a member, by CLEAPSS. See also the Association for Science Education publication *Be safe! some aspects of safety in school science and technology for Key Stages 1 and 2* (2nd edition, 1990). This contains more detailed advice than can be included here.

The points listed below require particular attention.

Take care that children do not look directly at the Sun. They could be blinded by looking at it through binoculars or a telescope.

If children are asked to observe the night sky, this should be done under the close supervision of a responsible adult.

2.1 Time

AREAS FOR INVESTIGATION

◆ Finding out about different units of time.

◆ Investigating the timing of events, using a variety of timers.

◆ Investigating shadows as a means of telling the time.

KEY IDEAS

◆ It takes a day, 24 hours, for the Earth to spin round once.

◆ It takes a year, 365 ¼ days, for the Earth to orbit the Sun.

◆ *Measurement of time as days, weeks and months is based on the relative positions of the Earth, Sun and Moon.

(*Asterisks indicate ideas which will be developed more fully in later key stages.)

A LOOK AT time

The movements of the Earth and the Moon are used to measure time.

◆ The Earth travels around the Sun in 1 year (365 ¼ days).
◆ The Moon travels around the Earth in 4 weeks (almost 1 month).
◆ The Earth spins round in 1 day (24 hours).

Timing devices help us to keep an accurate track of time.

Finding out children's ideas

STARTER ACTIVITIES

To find out children's ideas about time, you could ask:

How long is a day?
How long is a month?
How long is a year?
Which things help us to tell what time of day it is?

Children could draw and talk about some of the things that help us to tell:

◆ what time of day it is;
◆ which day of the week it is;
◆ which year it is.

If you didn't have a watch or clock, how would you know what time it is?

Children's ideas

Many children will have heard of the units of time we use, such as minutes, hours, days, weeks, months and years; but they tend to find it difficult to gauge the length of these periods.

When asked about the length of the units of time we use, many children give either no answer at all, or an arbitrary number. Here are some typical responses to questions about time:

How long is a day?

> *I don't know.*
> *5 minutes.*
> *12 hours.*

How long is a month?

> *I don't know.*
> *16 hours.*
> *7 days.*

How long is a year?

> *I don't know.*
> *15 hours.*
> *12 months.*

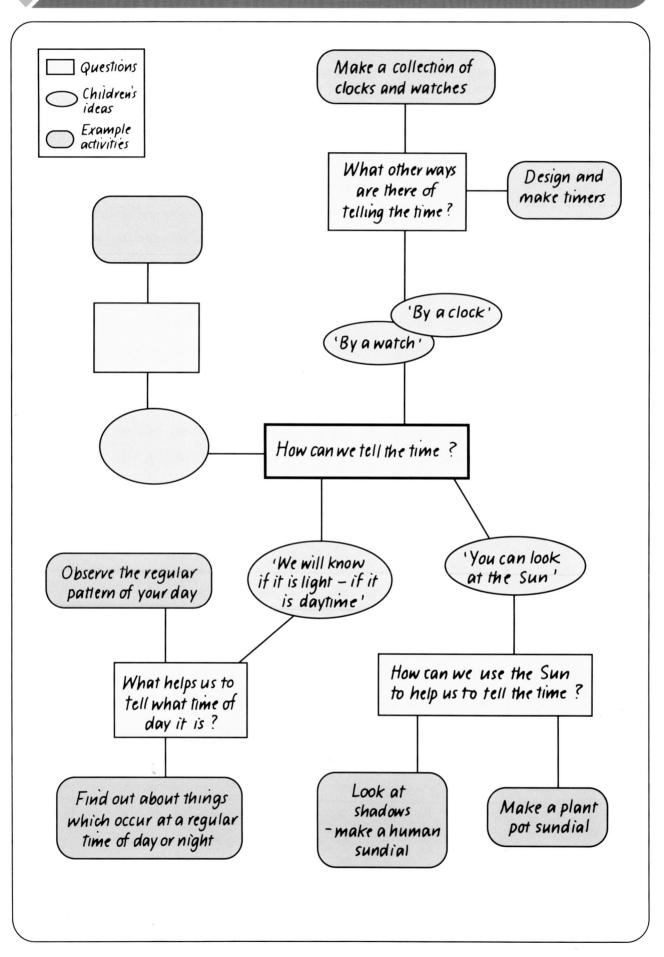

Questions

Children's ideas

Example activities

Make a collection of clocks and watches

What other ways are there of telling the time?

Design and make timers

'By a clock'

'By a watch'

How can we tell the time?

Observe the regular pattern of your day

'We will know if it is light – if it is daytime'

'You can look at the Sun'

What helps us to tell what time of day it is?

How can we use the Sun to help us to tell the time?

Find out about things which occur at a regular time of day or night

Look at shadows – make a human sundial

Make a plant pot sundial

Helping children to develop their ideas

The chart opposite shows how you can help children to develop their ideas from starting points which have given rise to different ideas.

The use of the word 'day' often refers to daylight hours or to the time we are awake. When we come to use the word in a more scientific way – for example, when explaining day-time and night-time – children will need to understand that we mean a 24-hour cycle of day and night. There is no way of not using the word 'day' in both senses, and often we have to explain which one is meant.

1 Days of the week

Help children learn the order of the days of the week, and the months of the year, by encouraging them to associate particular days or months with an event.

2 Months of the year

Help children to learn the months of the year.

They could make a chart showing the months of the year. They could take this home so that their families can help them to fill in any special events. These might include family birthdays, festivals and holidays.

A first look at Time and Space shows some of the special events that occur in the year of a family, and could provide a starting point for this activity.

3 Telling the time

Make a varied collection of clocks, watches, calendars, diaries and so on, so that the children can discuss and explain how they would use them.

e

Q *How can we tell what time it is?*

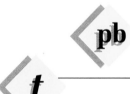
pb

Children could look at the timing devices shown in *A first look at Time and Space* and discuss how we use them.

t

There are regular patterns which we can observe to help us keep track of time

Get the children to think about how the regular events in the day and night help us to know the time.

Some of their suggestions might include:

♦ whether it is light or dark;
♦ the sounds in the house;
♦ which television programme is on;
♦ bird or animal sounds;
♦ traffic sounds.

what time of day is it when...?

pb

A first look at Time and Space shows pictures of scenes and activities at different times which children could consider.

To help children to become more aware of the daily sequence of events, they could look around the school and their immediate environment for things that happen at particular times. The children could make a time line of their day, marking in regular activities. Or they could make separate drawings of significant events during the day and stick them in the right position on a large cut-out of a clock.

Q *How much time do you spend asleep?*
How long do you spend at school?
How much time do you spend at home?

Children could use a computer to show their findings in the form of a bar chart.

4 How long does it take?

Give children a collection of timers. Ask them to predict and then time how long it takes for them to complete a variety of tasks.

Q *How many cubes can you fit together before the [song ends]?*
How many times can you write your name before the [water runs out]?
How many beads can you thread before the [buzzer sounds]?
How many cats can you draw before the [second hand on the clock completes a full turn]?

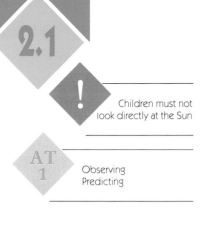

2.1

! Children must not look directly at the Sun

AT 1 Observing Predicting

5 Recording shadows at different times of the day

On a clear sunny day, the children could go into the playground and look at their shadows. They can work in pairs to draw round each other's shadow. They should mark the position of their feet carefully, so that they can come back later and draw where the shadow has moved to. They should note down the time they drew their shadow each time.

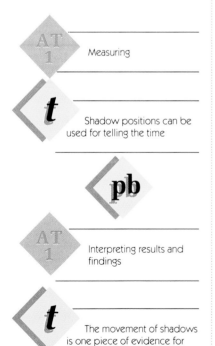

AT 1 Measuring

t Shadow positions can be used for telling the time

pb

AT 1 Interpreting results and findings

t The movement of shadows is one piece of evidence for the daily rotation of the Earth

 What do you think will happen to your shadow if we come back to look at it later?

Encourage children to measure the length of the shadow as well as noting its change in position. They could also note the position of the Sun in the sky.

A first look at Time and Space shows a child acting as a simple shadow clock, and also gives a list of Roman numbers.

Q *Why do you think your shadow moves?*
Why are the shadows different lengths at different times of the day?

To help children understand that changes are regular, the shadow record can be used as a clock the following day and checked against clocks in school.

AREAS FOR INVESTIGATION

◆ Exploring Space by observing the night sky, particularly the Moon.

◆ Observing the position of the Sun in the sky.

◆ Comparing day-time activities with night-time activities.

◆ Finding explanations of day and night.

◆ Looking at pictures of the Sun and Moon.

KEY IDEAS

◆ The positions of the Sun and the Moon in the sky change throughout the day and night.

◆ *Night occurs because the Earth spins. At any time half the Earth is illuminated by the Sun, and the other half is in shade.

(*Asterisks indicate ideas which will be developed more fully in later key stages.)

A LOOK AT the Earth, Sun and Moon

The Earth spins round once each day. As our part of the Earth turns away from the Sun we experience sunset, then nightfall.

The Sun, the Moon and the Earth are large, separate bodies. The Sun provides the heat and light for living things on Earth.

The Moon goes round the Earth in roughly four weeks. We can see the Moon in the night sky because it reflects light from the Sun. When the Moon is in the day sky we can see it faintly, or not at all. Over a four-week cycle, the Moon goes through 'phases' caused by its position relative to the Earth and the Sun.

The Moon rises later each day because of the combined effects of the Earth's spin and the Moon's own motion round it.

Finding out children's ideas
■ STARTER ACTIVITIES

1 Thinking about night and day

Ask the children to draw a picture to show why night and day happen. You might probe their ideas further.

Q *What happens to the Sun during the day?*
Can you tell me how night happens?
What happens to the Sun at night?

Q *What does the Moon look like at night?*
What do you think happens to the Moon in the day-time?
Does the Moon always look the same?

Children who suggest that the appearance of the Moon changes could show their ideas in a picture. Can these children suggest how long it takes for these changes to occur?

2 The shape and size of the Earth, Sun and Moon

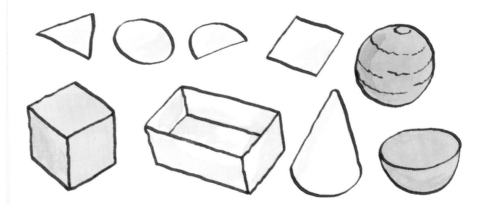

Give the children a range of two-dimensional and three-dimensional shapes.

Q *What shape is the Earth?*
What shape is the Sun?
What shape is the Moon?

When the children have chosen the shapes discuss why they have made these choices.

Q *What makes you think that the Earth is this shape?*
What makes you think that the Sun is this shape?
What makes you think that the Moon is this shape?

Ask the children to draw a picture of what they might see out of a spaceship window.

Q *You go up in a spaceship and look out of the window.*
What do you think you might see?

Children's ideas

1 Children's explanations of why night happens

Children generally explain night in terms of their own needs.

> *We've got to go to bed.*
> *To get some sleep.*
> *We have night because our bodies need rest. When we have day-time other countries have night-time.*

Some children suggest that the Sun moves elsewhere at night and the Moon moves closer.

> *The Sun's on the other side of the world.*
> *The Moon comes up the Sun goes down*
> *The Sun goes behind the clouds.*
> *The Sun goes away into the dark – it reflects on the Moon..*

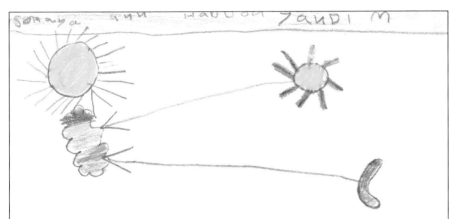

The Sun comes out of the clouds in the day and the Moon comes out of the clouds at night.

Some children explain what happens to the Sun in anthropomorphic terms:

> *It goes to bed.*
> *It goes to sleep.*

Very few children link the apparent movement of the Sun across the sky with the rotation of the Earth, as in this example:

> *The Sun moves because the world turns and the Sun goes from one place to another place.*

Some children are aware that the appearance of the Moon changes, but some believe there is more than one Moon.

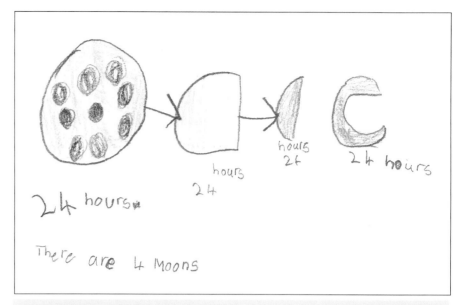

It goes to the cloud and comes out, it goes into the cloud again and comes back as a banana shape. It takes four minutes.

2 The shape and size of the Earth, Sun and Moon

In response to the question about the shape of the Earth children mainly choose round shapes, although these are sometimes discs rather than spheres. It could be that the children concentrate on 'roundness' without discriminating between two dimensional shapes and the less familiar three dimensional ones.

The reasons children give for choosing these shapes are:

> *It is round.*
> *It is big and round.*
> *Because it goes round and round.*
> *The world looks like a ball – I've got a globe at home.*

Many children think that the Sun is smaller than the Earth, because it appears smaller as they view it in the sky. They choose a small ball to represent the Sun and a larger ball to represent the Earth.

In pictures of what they might see in Space children often represent things in a familiar way. They may show the Moon as a crescent, the Sun surrounded by 'beams' or the stars as pointed objects.

Some very young children may know that the Sun is further from the Earth than is the Moon.

Children may know particular facts as this child shows in his description of what he might see from a spaceship window.

However, when thinking about Space, some children may include fictional characters.

Some children will show an awareness of different planets in their drawings.

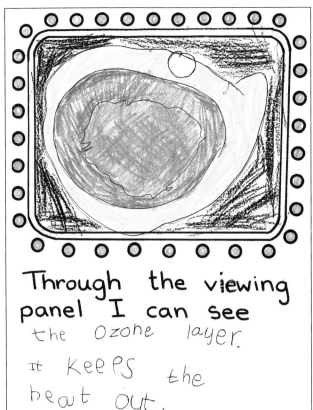

Through the viewing panel I can see the ozone layer. It keeps the heat out.

Earth it's round

Flying Monster

Space ship

Moon

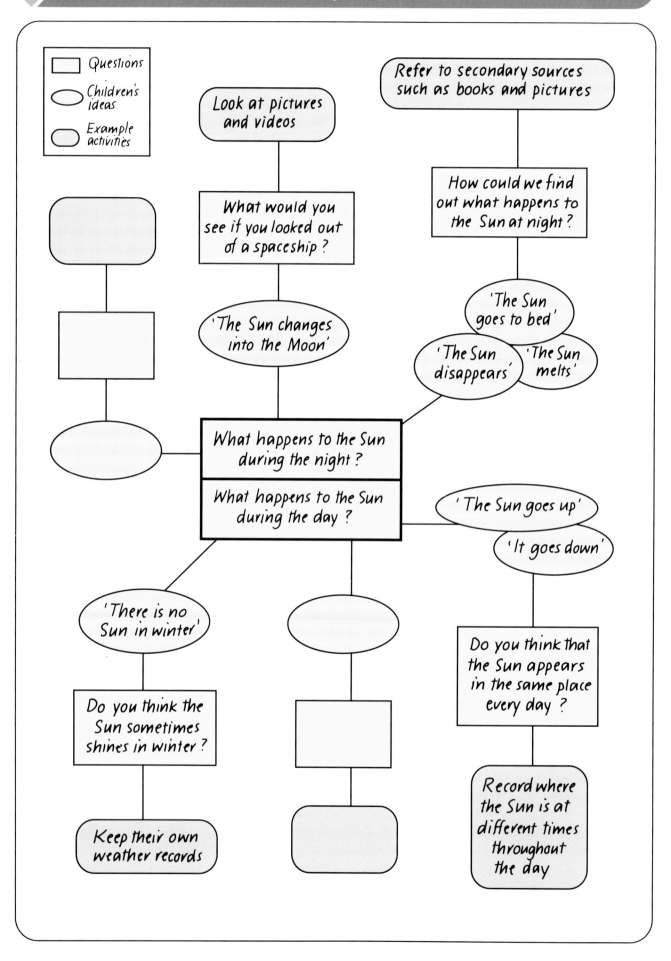

Questions

Children's ideas

Example activities

Look at pictures and videos

Refer to secondary sources such as books and pictures

What would you see if you looked out of a spaceship?

How could we find out what happens to the Sun at night?

'The Sun changes into the Moon'

'The Sun goes to bed'

'The Sun disappears'

'The Sun melts'

What happens to the Sun during the night?

What happens to the Sun during the day?

'The Sun goes up'

'It goes down'

'There is no Sun in winter'

Do you think the Sun sometimes shines in winter?

Do you think that the Sun appears in the same place every day?

Keep their own weather records

Record where the Sun is at different times throughout the day

Helping children to develop their ideas

The chart on the previous page shows how you can help children to develop their ideas from starting points which have given rise to different ideas.

1 Differences between night and day

Get the children to identify the main differences between day and night. They could do this by drawing 'things which happen at night' on one side of the page and 'things which happen during the day' on the other side.

Encourage them to think about changes in the street, plant and animal life, the sky and so on.

When they have done this they could discuss their ideas with each other.

The descriptions of the night life of a town fox and of people who are awake during the night, provided in *A first look at Time and Space*, might help children to think of some of these changes.

2 Making a 'night corner' in the classroom

The children could make a 'night corner' in the classroom by adapting the role play area or by using a large cardboard box or playhouse. They could make their own models of animals and birds which are active during the night as well as a model moon.

The children could also think of ways to light their night scene.

Q *Is there any light at night?*
Where does it come from?

Encourage them to light the model Moon with reflected light using a torch or small bulb and a reflective surface, such as white paper. To help them towards this idea, ask:

Q *How does the Moon get its light?*
Can you make the Moon in the night corner shine?

(See the *Electricity and magnetism* and *Light* teachers' guides for activities on simple electric circuits, and reflecting light.)

3 A classroom 'Space station'

This could provide the stimulus for discussions about what it would be like to be in Space.

Q *What would the Earth, Sun and Moon look like from the Space station?*

The children could paint pictures or make models to show what they would see from the spacecraft. They could use the pictures as the 'windows' of the spacecraft or place them around the room so that they could see them as they look out from the spacecraft.

It may be interesting for the children to see some short video clips of the Apollo flights, so that they can see what the Moon and Earth look like from Space.

A first look at Time and Space contains information about people landing on the Moon, and photographs of the Moon taken from Earth and from the Apollo spacecraft. It also provides information about the night sky.

The children could also get information from large, colourful pictures or books which use fairly simple text. If the children refer to these secondary sources with their own ideas already in mind, they are more likely to extract useful information.

Children could find out more about Space by observing the night sky. Parents could be encouraged to join in children's exploration of Space and to take them out to look at it.

 Children observing the night sky should be supervised. Take the opportunity to warn children never to observe the Sun through a telescope or binoculars. This could blind them. It is all right to look at the Moon

Children could look for pictures showing how the Sun and Moon are represented in story books.

Q *Do the pictures in story books always show the Moon and Sun as they really are?*

Amy's granny had told her many stories about the Man in the Moon and now here he was, looking at Amy through her bedroom window and smiling! This is what Amy saw....

4 Observing the Sun

The sun comes up opposite my bedroom window. It was light at 7.30 a.m.

Get the children to discuss their ideas about what happens to the Sun during one day.

Q *Which window is the sun shining through into our classroom?*
Where do you think the Sun might shine later on today?

 Children should not look directly at the Sun. Warn children never to observe the Sun through a telescope or binoculars. This could blind them

AT
1
Observing
Interpreting results
and findings

Ask them to think how they could investigate their ideas.

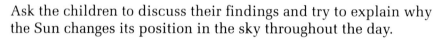

Ask the children to discuss their findings and try to explain why the Sun changes its position in the sky throughout the day.

Q *What ideas do other people have about the Sun?*

it

Children could use a tape recorder to record interviews

They could hear about the stories told in different cultures to explain the apparent movement of the Sun and Moon, and the changing shape of the Moon. Many native American, Caribbean and other folk tales illustrate the ways in which people have tried to explain their ideas about day and night.

pb

In A first look at Time and Space there is an Aboriginal folk tale about the Moon, and information about the importance of the Sun and Moon in festivals and celebrations from different cultures.

e

5 **Finding out about the Earth**

A large inflatable globe
will stimulate discussion
about the Earth.

The children could find:

AT
1
Communicating

◆ where the seas are;
◆ where Britain is;
◆ countries they have
   visited;
◆ where their relatives
   live;
◆ countries in the news;
◆ hot regions;
◆ cold regions.

In a class discussion encourage children to think about their own ideas about the shape of the Earth alongside globes and pictures of the Earth.

 What would happen to people if the Earth was round like a plate?

Try sticking cardboard people on the globe so that they are neither upright nor upside down.

 Could people live in these places on Earth?
Where else might people live on Earth?
Where is the ground for these people?
Where is 'up' for these people?
How do they manage to stay on Earth?

6 Using models

Children could select shapes that help them to explain what happens to the Earth, Sun and Moon during day and night.

 Can you show how night and day happen with your shape?
Can you show what happens to the Earth and Sun in one day?
Is the Earth spinning, or does it stay still?

Encourage children to share their ideas in a class discussion. You might use the shapes to show children the movement of the Earth, Moon and Sun. Asking questions will help children consider the model alongside their own ideas.

 Which part of the Earth will be having day-time?
Which part of the Earth will be having night-time?
Can you see the Moon during the day?
Can you see the Sun at night?

t Night happens because the Earth turns away from the Sun

AT 1   Observing
Communicating

2.3 Seasonal change

AREAS FOR INVESTIGATION

◆ Exploring differences between summer and winter.

◆ Investigating the ways living things respond to seasonal change.

◆ Keeping weather records, and finding out how the weather affects human activities.

KEY IDEAS

◆ Plant, animal and human activities vary according to the season.

◆ During the summer, the Sun is higher in the sky and the weather is warmer.

A LOOK AT seasonal change

Each day, from winter to summer, the Sun rises a little earlier in the morning and sets later at night, the path of the Sun across the sky becomes higher, and the days get warmer. These trends are reversed from summer to winter.

In the spring animals become more active, many are born, and plants that appeared to be dead during the winter now begin to grow. Plant growth continues through the summer to the autumn, and many animals that were born in the spring are now fully grown. As autumn approaches, the weather becomes cooler, leaves fall from the trees and some birds fly to warmer places.

During the year our daily lives are affected by the seasons. For example, we may do much of our work indoors and wear warm clothes during the winter, and take our holidays and engage in outdoor pursuits in summer.

Finding out children's ideas

■ STARTER ACTIVITIES

Give the children a large piece of paper divided into two, so they can draw and write about 'summer things' on one side and 'winter things' on the other.

 How is a summer day different from a winter day?

Ask the children to draw a summer picture and a winter picture showing the Sun in each.

Have the children noticed the different position of the Sun in the sky in summer and winter?

Children's ideas

The following are typical examples of differences children notice between summer and winter.

Winter

> *It's cold and raining.*
> *The Sun's in Australia.*
> *It's darker earlier in the winter.*
> *Winter is cold, you can run and slip.*
> *Leaves fall off the trees.*

Summer

> *The Sun only comes in summer, and a little bit in winter.*
> *In summer you can go to the beach.*
> *In summer you wear a T-shirt.*
> *In summer the Sun shines, in winter it doesn't.*

2.3

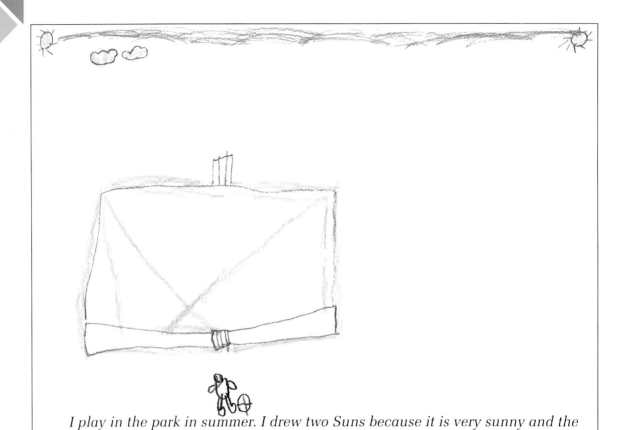

I play in the park in summer. I drew two Suns because it is very sunny and the other came from another country.

You can find insects.
A summer day is longer.

Winter | Spring | Summer | Autumn

Draw yourself in the park in each season.

Most children refer to the difference in temperature – hot summers and cold winters. Some notice the differences in plant and animal activity; only a few children mention day length.

Winter | Spring | Summer | Autumn

Draw yourself in the park in each season.

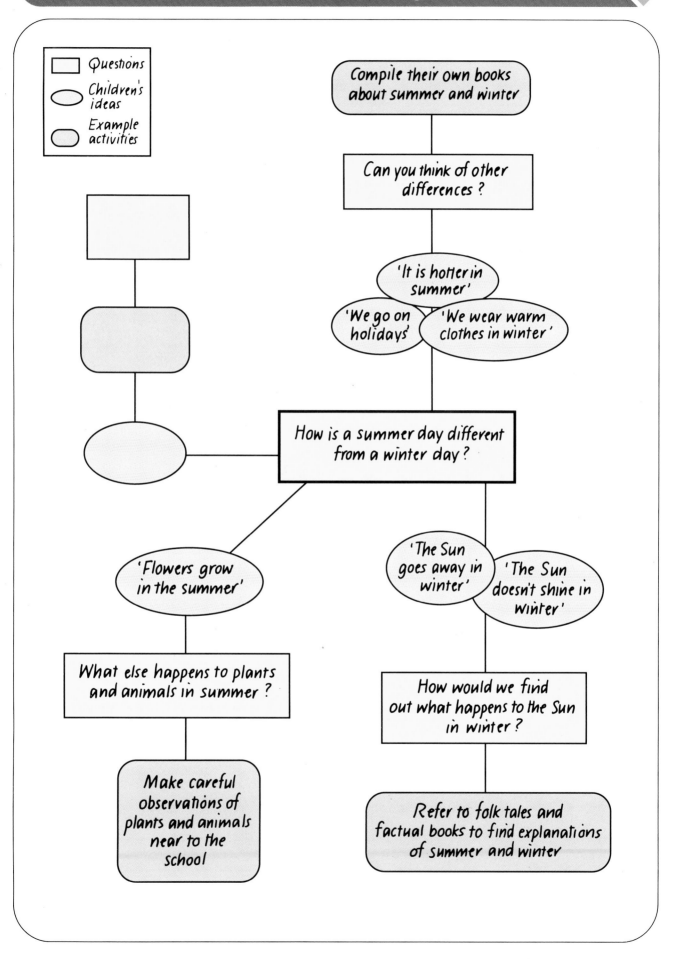

Questions

Children's ideas

Example activities

Compile their own books about summer and winter

Can you think of other differences?

'It is hotter in summer'

'We go on holidays'

'We wear warm clothes in winter'

How is a summer day different from a winter day?

'Flowers grow in the summer'

'The Sun goes away in winter'

'The Sun doesn't shine in winter'

What else happens to plants and animals in summer?

How would we find out what happens to the Sun in winter?

Make careful observations of plants and animals near to the school

Refer to folk tales and factual books to find explanations of summer and winter

Helping children to develop their ideas

The chart on the previous page shows how you can help children to develop their ideas from starting points which have given rise to different ideas.

1 The seasons: plant and animal activity

A school garden or 'wild area' can provide many opportunities for observing seasonal change; for example, the children could focus on a small area in which there is a tree, and note the changes, record the tree's growth and describe the weather at regular intervals throughout the year.

t A wildlife area will need careful planning and a lot of support from other people, including the school governors and possibly the LEA. Children should be encouraged to recognize that the area will need to be constantly maintained

! Check the area for absence of dog mess, broken glass, and poisonous plants. Beware of buried pipes and cables

AT 1 Observing

Children will learn to associate the various stages in plants' life cycles with the time of year, temperature and day length. (See the *Living things in their environment* and *Living processes* teachers' guides.)

t Plants and animals change through the seasons

2 Human activity

Through class discussion, help the children think about how their own activities relate to seasonal change.

 What do you usually do when you go home from school? Do you think you would do the same things if it were summer/winter? Which things can you only do in summer? Which things can you only do in winter?

(For further work on weather, see the *Rocks, soil and weather* teachers' guide.)

3 Noting the position of the Sun in the sky

The children may think that we do not have any sunshine during the winter months.

Get the children to keep their own weather records. The activity could last for one or two weeks, and may be particularly helpful to children if it takes place in winter.

Children could record their observations on a computer, using a simple data base.

 What do you think has happened to the Sun when we can't see it in the sky? Where do you think the Sun is today?

At different times throughout the year the children could draw pictures to show the position of the midday Sun.

4 Plant life

Because many fruits and vegetables are found in supermarkets throughout the year, children may be unaware that they are seasonal.

Make a collection of different fruits and vegetables, and ask children to try to discover where some of them come from. (Imported fruits are often labelled with their country of origin.)

2.3

AT 1 — Communicating

! Children should not look directly at the Sun. Warn children not to observe the Sun through a telescope or binoculars. This could blind them

 *it*

AT 1 — Observing

t During the summer the Sun is higher in the sky

 e

 e

Children could draw, paint, or make a collage of pictures of the fruits and vegetables.

 Q *Why do we need to bring fruits and vegetables from such faraway places?*

They could use a globe to find the place where each kind comes from.

In Britain, food is plentiful all year round, and the 'Harvest Festival' has practically lost its original meaning. However, the idea of harvest could be used to focus on the seasonal availability of many foods, both in the past and in other countries where people still depend on a successful local harvest for their food.

5   Sorting pictures

Children could sort a large collection of pictures into sets, showing which ones they associate with spring, summer, autumn and winter. There could be other pictures in the collection showing activities that could take place throughout the year.

 pb

In *A first look at Time and Space* there are photographs of scenes and activities which can be associated with seasons.

Children could listen to poems that refer to the seasons of the year, or they could write their own poems.

CHAPTER 3

Assessment

3.1 Introduction

You will have been assessing your children's ideas and skills by using the activities in this teachers' guide. This on-going, formative assessment is essentially part of teaching since what you find is immediately used in suggesting the next steps to help the children's progress. But this information can also be brought together and summarized for purposes of recording and reporting progress. This summary of performance has to be in terms of National Curriculum level descriptions at the end of the key stages, and some schools keep records in terms of levels at other times.

This chapter helps you summarize the information you have from children's work in terms of level descriptions. Examples of work relating to the theme of this guide are discussed and features which indicate activity at a certain level are pointed out to show what to look for in your pupils' work as evidence of achievement at one level or another. It is necessary, however, to look across the full range of work, and not judge from any single event or piece of work.

There are two sets of examples provided. The first is the assessment of skills in the context of the activities related to the concepts covered in this guide. The second deals with the development of these concepts.

3.2 Assessment of skills (AT1)

> Things to look out for when pupils are investigating the Earth in Space as indicating progress from level 1 to level 3:
>
> **Level 1**: Making observations of the Sun, Moon and stars in the sky, such as their position and shape; talking about and drawing them.
>
> **Level 2**: Making suggestions as well as responding to others' suggestions about how to find things out about the shape and movement of objects in the sky. Using equipment, such as globes, clocks and 2-D and 3-D geometric shapes, to make observations. Recording what they find and comparing it with what they expected.
>
> **Level 3**: Saying what they expect to happen when something changes and suggesting ways of collecting information to test their predictions. Carrying out fair tests, knowing why they are fair, and making measurements. Recording what they find in a variety of ways; noticing any patterns in it.

Over the spring and summer terms a Year 2 teacher took groups of children into the school playground to observe the apparent movement of the Sun across the sky. A group observed the Sun on eight separate occasions, over a two-day period. Each day the children recorded their observations on an outline picture.

The teacher always accompanied the groups to remind children not to look directly at the Sun, and to help those who had difficulty with their observations.

41

The following description shows how a group of children including Angela and Chirag carried out their observations over a two-day period.

Day one:

Before they observed the Sun the children told the teacher that they knew the Sun moved in the sky, but were unable to give more detail.

In the playground, the teacher discussed the outline picture with each child, helped all the children to mark the position of the Sun and asked them to predict where the Sun would be at break-time. The children repeated their observations at break-time, and predicted the position of the Sun at lunch-time. Observations and predictions were repeated at lunch-time and the end of the school day. The teacher took the children to the same spot in the playground whenever they observed the Sun.

At the end of the day children described what they had found out about the movement of the Sun. The teacher asked the children to predict where the Sun would be the next morning. After a brief discussion, they told the teacher that it would be 'in the other playground' - a playground on the opposite side of the school to the one in which they made their observations.

Day two:

The observations and predictions were repeated, and the children again described the movement of the Sun. Finally, the children predicted where the Sun would be on the following day at the start of school, break-time and at the end of the school day.

The children recorded their observations and predictions on the outline picture as follows:

Before school	Sun's position marked as	Predicted position at break-time marked as
	Morning sun	B
Break-time	Sun's position marked as	Predicted position at lunch-time marked as
	break sun	L
Lunch-time	Sun's position marked as	Predicted position at the end of school marked as
	lunch sun	E
End of school day	Sun's position marked as	
	end sun	

Day 1

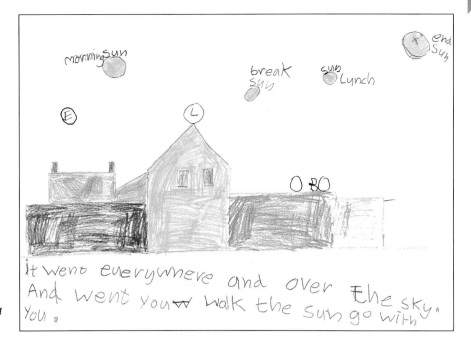

morning sun

break sun

sun Lunch

end Sun

O BO

Angela

it went everywhere and over the sky. And went you walk the sun go with you.

Chirag

morning sun

Sun

Break Sun

Lunch SUN

Lu

end sun

Chirag

I found out when you go to a house and you was looking at the sun it moves somewere else.

Day 2

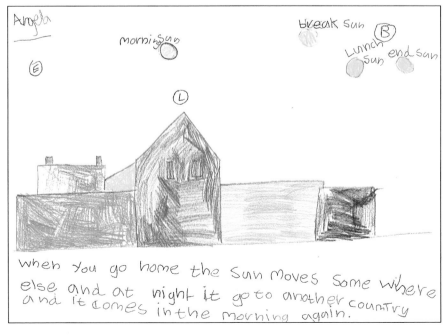

Angela

morning Sun

break sun

Lunch sun end sun

Angela

when you go home the sun moves some where else and at night it go to another country and it comes in the morning again.

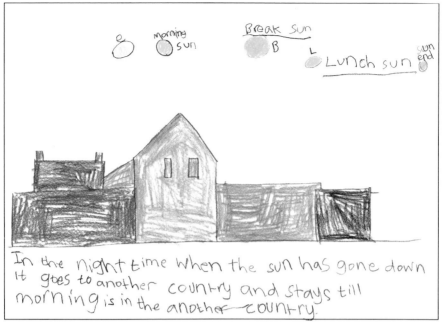

In the night time when the sun has gone down It goes to another country and stays till morning is in the another country.

Chirag

Final predictions

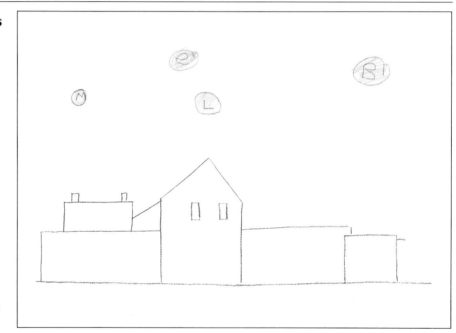

Angela

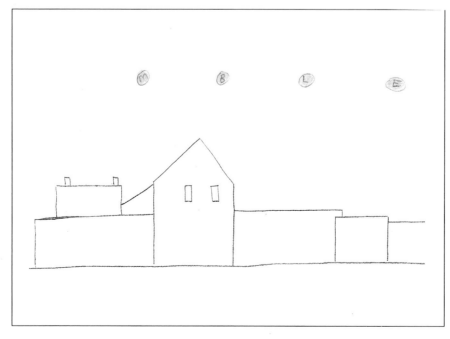

Chirag

Under the direction of their teacher, the children made observations of the Sun's position. They wrote about and discussed their observations. Thus their work meets the requirements at level 1. The extent to which it goes beyond this is a little difficult to assess because of the directed nature of the work.

Young children making a series of observations stretching over a relatively long time period are likely to require their teacher's assistance. They could be expected to work more independently in investigations which are less demanding of their personal organisation than the one presented here. Nevertheless, within the structure provided by the teacher they compared what they expected with what they found. They predicted that the Sun would move in the sky. This indication of work at level 2 would need to be confirmed by evidence of the children making predictions and observations without so much teacher support.

At the end of day one, the children did not indicate that they had perceived a pattern in their observations, nor were they aware of the Sun's 24-hour cycle.

However, on day two, after observing the position of the 'morning sun', Chirag appears to use his observations from the previous day accurately to predict the Sun's position at break-time. He appears to continue predicting in this way throughout day two. His final predictions again indicate the use of his observations to support predictions, an indication of work at level 2.

Chirag also appears to be aware of the Sun's 24-hour cycle at the end of the exploration.

Angela does not appear to have perceived a pattern in the apparent movement of the Sun across the day-time sky. However, by the end of the exploration, it is possible that she was aware of the Sun's 24-hour cycle - indicated by her final prediction for the 'morning sun'. Even though this one prediction may indicate that she is using her observations to predict, there would have to be more evidence that she uses her observations in this way for her work to be at level 2.

The teacher would have to think of other ways in which Angela could become more aware of the apparent movement of the Sun. For example, Angela could observe how the Sun shines into a classroom over a day. This simple exploration might also provide Angela with opportunities to become more aware of how observations can be interpreted, and to practise her interpretation skills.

3.3 Assessment of children's understanding (Part of AT 4)

> In terms of work relating to the Earth in Space, progression from level 1 to level 3 is indicated by:
>
> **Level 1**: Identifying the Sun as a source of light and heat during the day.
>
> **Level 2**: Realising that the Sun, Moon and stars are objects in space outside the Earth and, like the Earth, are three-dimensional, not flat objects against a flat sky.
>
> **Level 3**: Realising that the positions of things in the sky change in a regular manner and using the patterns to predict roughly the position of the Sun in the sky; describing the variations in the shape of the Moon from one night to the next.

Both Angela and Chirag, in their writing, link the beginning of daylight with the arrival of the Sun and the beginning of night-time with the Sun going down. Further discussion would clarify the extent to which they see the end of daylight as a result of the disappearance of the Sun, thus indicating level 1, or just coincidental with it.

The children in a Year 2 class had been talking about 'living in Space' and the teacher took the opportunity to find out about their ideas on the Earth, Sun and Moon. She asked the children to draw pictures of what they thought they would see looking out of a spaceship window. As the children worked, the teacher asked some of the children to describe their pictures.

Katie's drawing (shown opposite) indicates that the Sun, Moon and Earth are separate bodies. Her description and representation of these bodies doesn't indicate that the bodies are spherical, as required of work at level 2. Young children often describe a spherical shape as 'round' and her meaning of the word would have to be discussed. Asking them to choose shapes to represent the Sun, Moon and Earth from a standard set of 2-D and 3-D shapes may help to clarify their meaning.

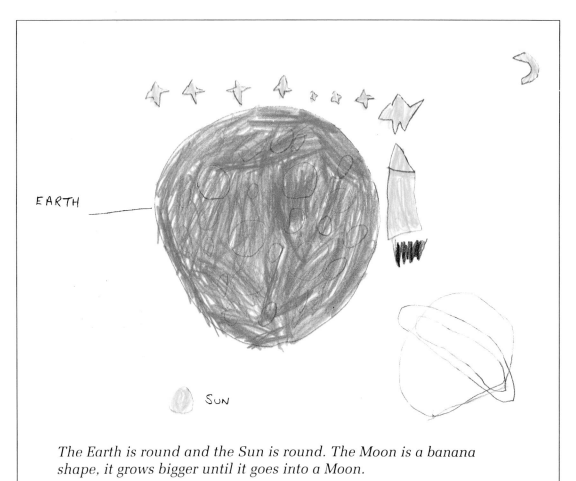

The Earth is round and the Sun is round. The Moon is a banana shape, it grows bigger until it goes into a Moon.

Katie

Harry was one of a group who observed and recorded the appearance of the Moon over a 4-week period. During this time cloud often covered the Moon, so the children could not make a series of uninterrupted observations. On occasions the children forgot to observe the Moon, and the teacher had to give them considerable encouragement.

At the end of the period of observation the children described what they had found out about the Moon.

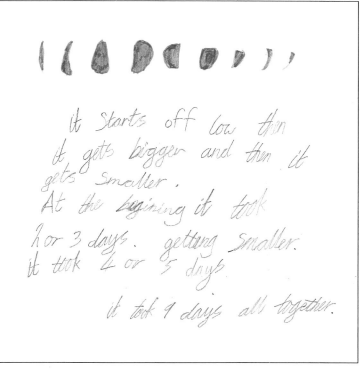

There are aspects of this work that Harry would have to develop further to meet the description at level 3. For example, the time periods suggested for the cycles are much too short. The teacher could help Harry's group to make progress towards level 3 by encouraging them to look more closely at their records of the appearance of the Moon or give them the opportunity of using models to explain how the Moon is illuminated by the Sun; or get them to collect daily information about the phases of the Moon from newspapers.

Harry

Index

NUFFIELD PRIMARY SCIENCE
Science Processes and Concept Exploration

Directors
Paul Black
Wynne Harlen

Deputy Director
Terry Russell

Project members
Robert Austin
Derek Bell
Adrian Hughes
Ken Longden
John Meadows
Linda McGuigan
Jonathan Osborne
Pamela Wadsworth
Dorothy Watt

First published 1993 by Collins Educational
An imprint of HarperCollins*Publishers*
77-85 Fulham Palace Road
London W6 8JB
Second edition published 1995
Reprinted 1996
Copyright © Nuffield-Chelsea Curriculum Trust 1993, 1995

ISBN 0 00 310245 9

Printed and bound in Italy by Rotolito Lombarda, Milan

Design by Carla Turchini, Chi Leung
Illustrations by Mike Dodd, Maureen Hallahan,
Tony Kenyon, Mary Lonsdale, Karen Tushingham,
Tony Wells
Cover artwork by Karen Tushingham

Photograph acknowledgements
Page 16: Zefa
Page 23: Science Photo Library
Page 34: Bubbles (x2)

Commissioned photography by Oliver Hatch

The Trust and the Publishers would like to thank the
governors, staff and pupils of Hillbrook Primary School,
Tooting, for their kind co-operation with many of the
photographs in this book.

Safety adviser
Peter Borrows

Other contributors
Marcella Armstrong
Anne de Normanville